THE
HUMAN
SKELETON

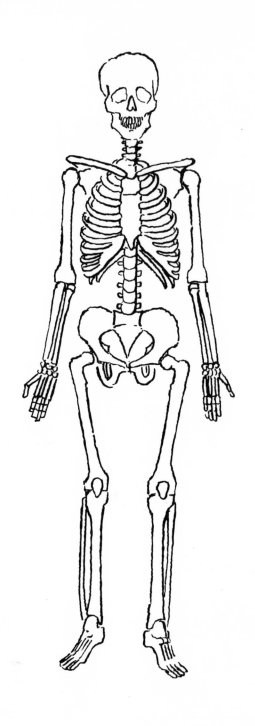

THE
HUMAN
SKELETON

Benjamin N. Schuman, M.D.

DRAWINGS BY

Michael K. Meyers

ATHENEUM   NEW YORK

1965

Text copyright © 1965 by Benjamin N. Schuman
Drawings copyright © 1965 by Michael K. Meyers
All rights reserved
Library of Congress catalog card number 65-21714
Published simultaneously in Canada by
    McClelland & Stewart Ltd.
Manufactured in the United States of America
Composition by The Composing Room, Inc., New York
Printed by Halliday Lithograph Corporation,
    West Hanover, Massachusetts
Bound by H. Wolff, New York
Design by David Rogers
First Edition

To Inge

INTRODUCTION

What does a spine really look like, and how can it be flexible enough to bend and yet stiff enough to hold a body erect? Why does a knee move back and not forward? Why does an arm rotate easily and not a leg? What permits the head to move up and down and around? How are the ribs attached to the spine and can they move? These are puzzling questions, and the answers are not always easy to find or to understand. This book begins with the spine and goes through all the major bones of the body, showing how each looks and works. It was written for anyone who is curious enough about his own bony framework to want to know something about it.

CONTENTS

THE
HUMAN
SKELETON

A man doesn't look like this,

or this.

He has a definite shape.

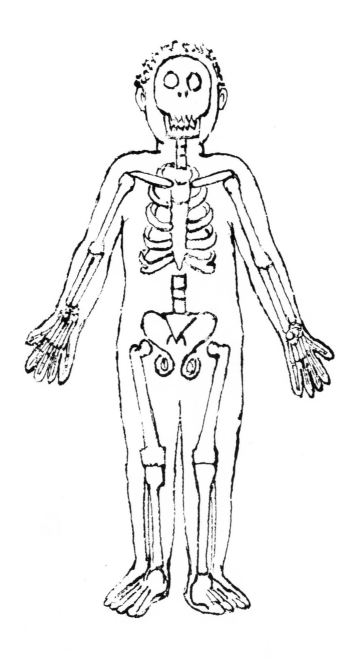

His skeleton gives him this shape.

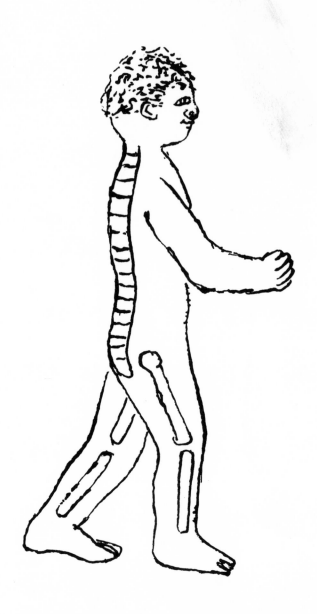

He can stand up by himself because
the bones of his back and legs hold him up.

THE SPINE

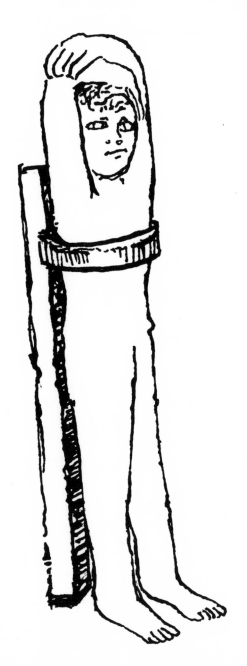

His spine or backbone holds the central part
of him upright, like a post.

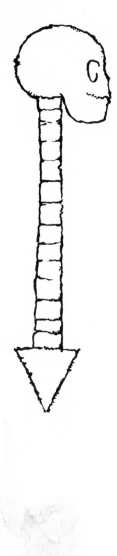

The skull rests on top of the spine.

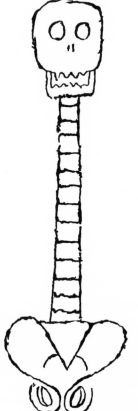

The bottom of the spine is like a spear sticking into the hip bones.

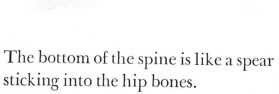

8

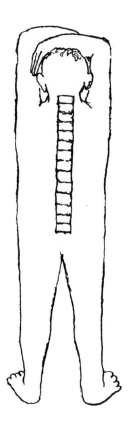

Though the spine looks like
a solid bone, it is not.

It is more like a stack of checkers.

There are soft pads or discs
in between the bones.

Each disc is like a
wad of chewing gum,
well chewed.

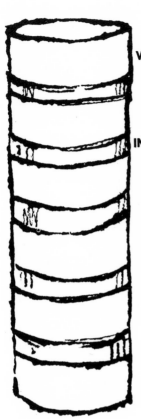

VERTEBRA

INTERVERTEBRAL DISC

Each bone in the spine is
called a vertebra.

And each of the soft discs
is called an intervertebral disc.

The entire column of vertebrae and
discs is called the vertebral column.

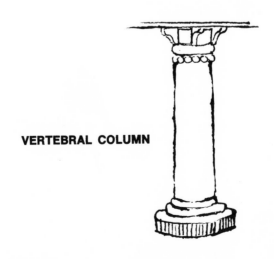

VERTEBRAL COLUMN

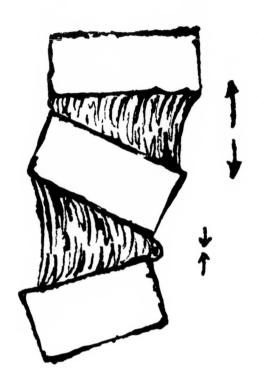

The discs can squeeze and stretch.
This makes the vertebral column flexible.

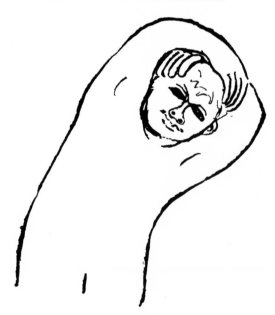

Therefore a man can bend his
body in many ways.

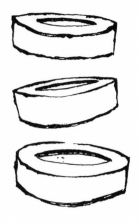

And just as the spine is not entirely like a post, the vertebrae are not really like solid checkers.

Each has a spike on one side and a hole beside the spike for the spinal cord.

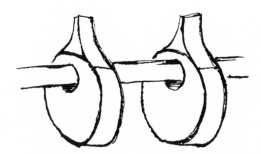

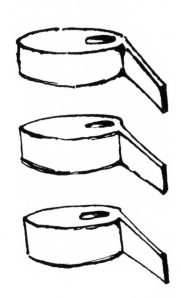

The spikes or spines of the vertebrae curve down.

When they are in position,
one over the other,
they overlap like
the scales of a dinosaur.

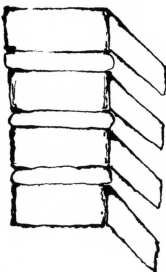

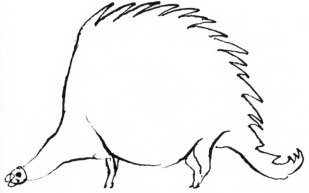

The hole for the spinal cord is
called the vertebral foramen. It is about
the size of a finger tip.

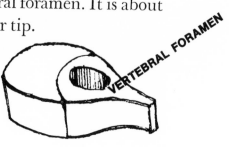

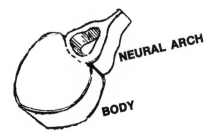

The vertebra, which is somewhat elongated,
is really in two parts: the neural arch,
which surrounds and protects the cord; and
the body, which bears weight.

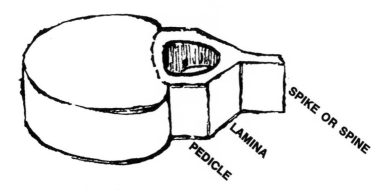

The part of the neural arch nearest the body
is called the pedicle (little foot).

The part farthest from the body is called
the lamina (little plate).

From the sides of the top of the arch,
two little bumpers face backwards.
On the bottom two more bumpers face forwards.

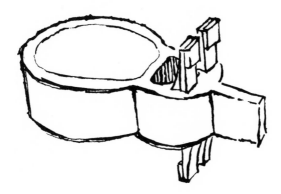

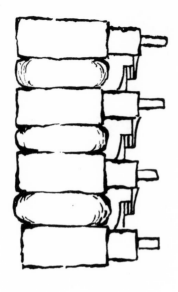

The bumpers of each vertebra
interlock, above and below,
with those of its neighbors
to prevent slipping.

A checker has become something far more complex.

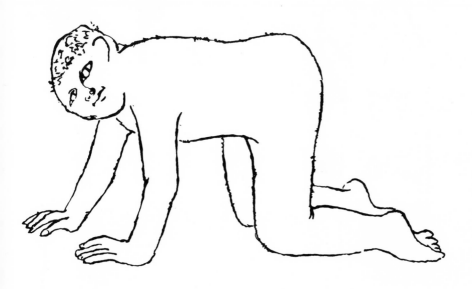

If a man walked on all fours, his ribs would hang down from his spine like a series of hoops.

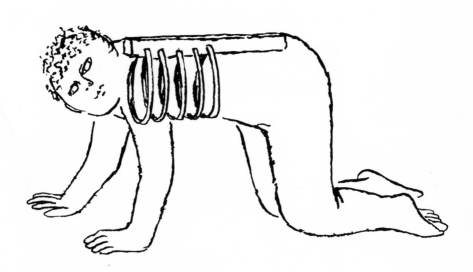

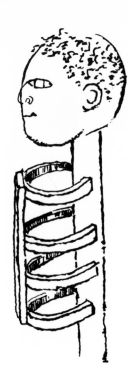

But a man stands upright. So his ribs stick out in front of his spine.

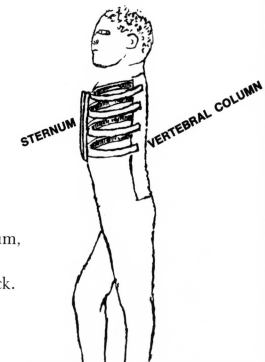

His breast bone, or sternum, is at the front, and his vertebral column is in back.

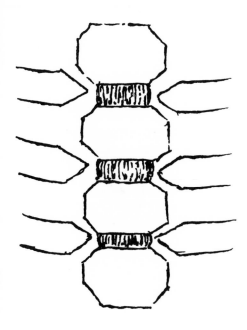

Each rib sticks onto an intervertebral disc
in the vertebral column.

Each rib comes out of a vertebra like a wing.

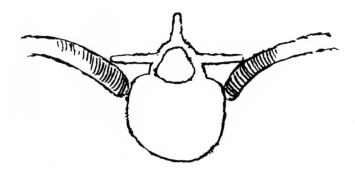

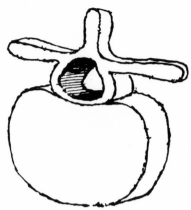

Each vertebra needs arms to brace
the rib or wing as it takes off.

From in front a vertebra
with its arms looks like this:

From the rear it looks like this:

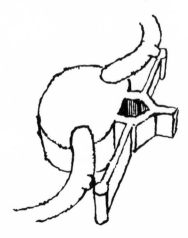

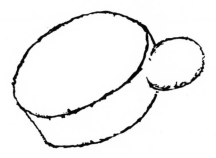

Any bony bump on a vertebra is called a process.

So the arms that brace the ribs
are called transverse processes.

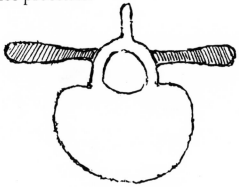

The anti-slip bumpers are called
articular processes.

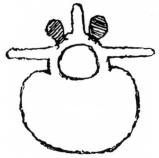

Reviewing all the processes:

ARTICULAR PROCESS

TRANSVERSE PROCESS
(seen end on)

ARTICULAR PROCESS

VERTEBRAL SPINE

The vertebrae fit very nicely together.

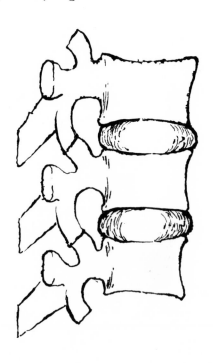

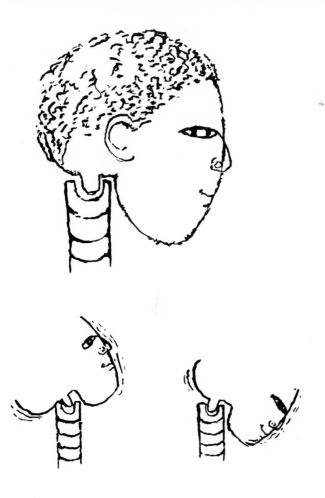

On top of the spine the skull moves back
and forth on a pair of rockers.

The rockers are built into
the base of the skull.

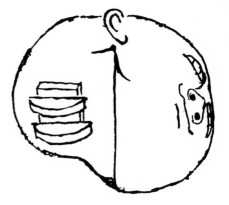

The top vertebra is different from the others because it must hold the skull.
It is a diamond-shaped vertebra and is called the atlas.

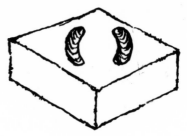

It has a hole in the center for the spinal cord.

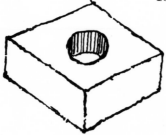

Next to the hole for the cord is a smaller hole, separated by a very tough ligament.

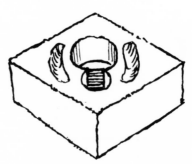

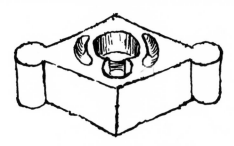

The atlas has no down curving spike to overlap at the back, and its ends flare out a bit.

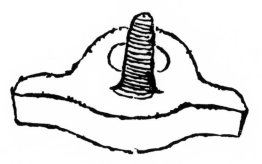

The vertebra below the atlas, which is called the axis, has a projection that fits into the extra hole in the atlas.

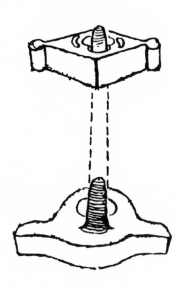

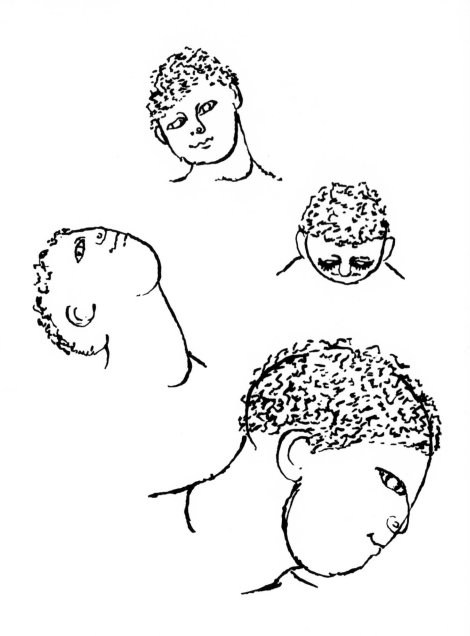

This arrangement makes for great flexibility.
It makes it possible to rubberneck.

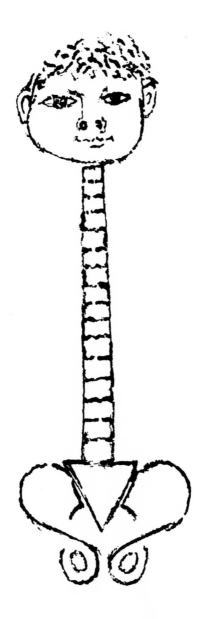

The opposite end of the spine, the sacrum,
is like a spear sticking into the hip bone.

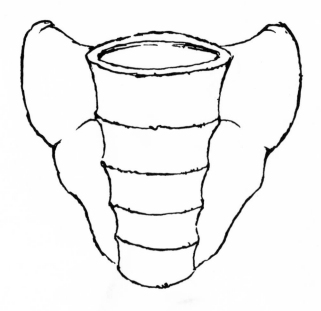

The sacrum consists of five vertebral bodies fused together with a mass of bone on either side.

A row of holes on either side marks the original boundaries between vertebrae before they were fused together. There are no discs.

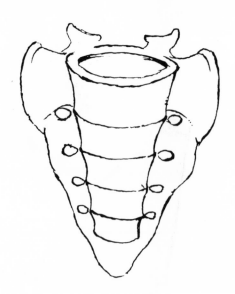

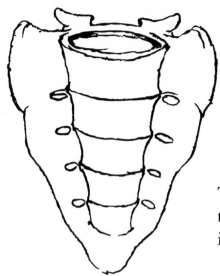

The bone mass on either side of the vertebrae in the sacrum is called the sacral ala or wings.

The edge of the ala has a surface that makes a joint with the pelvis. It is called the auricular surface (auricle means little ear).

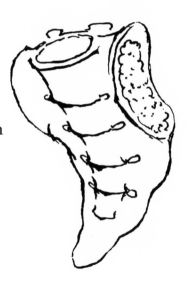

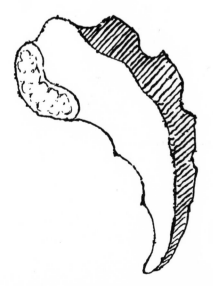

On the back of the sacrum is a ridge called the sacral crest.

CURVES OF THE SPINE

As an embryo lies curled up,
the spine is in a long, single curve.

Straightened out some at birth,
the spine still has two curves.
One is the chest or thoracic curve.
The other is the tailbone or sacral curve.

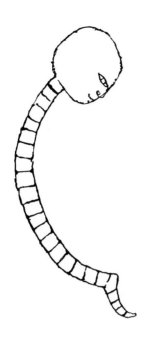

When a baby sits up,
his head points down.

When he looks straight ahead, his neck
curves back. This gives him the third
spinal curve, the cervical curve.

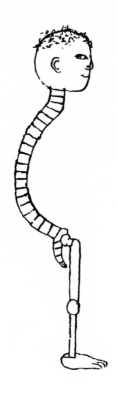

When a child begins to walk,
his hips are too far in front.

So he develops a fourth curve,
the curve at the small of the back,
the lumbar curve.

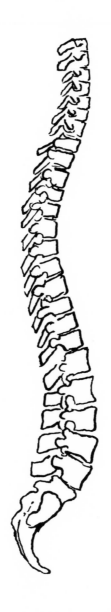

Here is a realistic drawing of
the complete vertebral column.

THE PELVIS

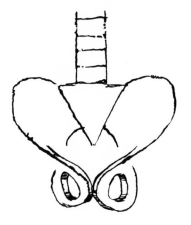

At the bottom of the spine, the sacrum attaches to the hip bone or pelvis.

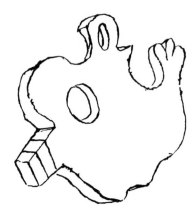

The hip bone has a funny shape. It doesn't look like anything, so it is called the innominate or nameless bone.

Basically the pelvis is a bucket for the guts or viscera.

To make a pelvis, first
knock the bottom out
of an old bucket.

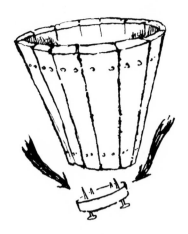

Then cut a notch in back
for the sacrum
and two holes in front.

Trim the front down.

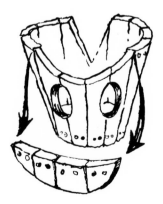

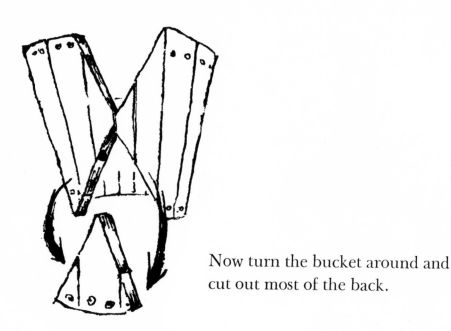

Now turn the bucket around and cut out most of the back.

From the back you can see the holes in front.

Chisel out a shallow socket for the thigh bone (the femur) at either side.

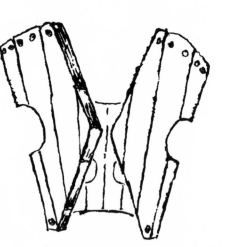

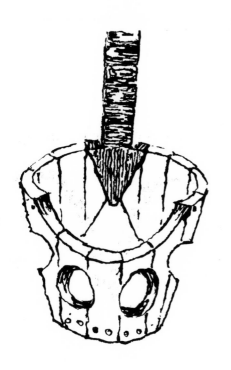

Then turn it around and stick the sacrum in the place made for it.

Put the femurs in their sockets, and the pelvis is complete.

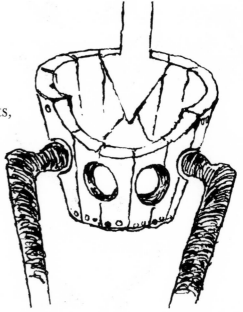

Another way to make a pelvis is to roll out
two flat slabs of clay.

Make them bigger on top.

Cut a hole in each one
at the bottom.

Twist each into
a figure eight.

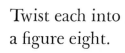

Now stick the two pieces together in front.

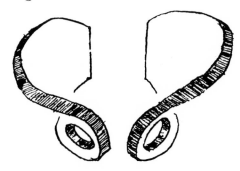

Roll out a little ledge in front and add
a socket for the femur on the side.

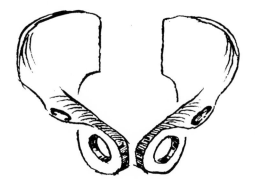

Now install the sacrum and
femurs and it's done.

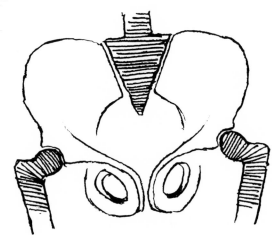

The top part of the pelvis, or
pelvic girdle as the pelvis is
sometimes called, is the ilium.

The rim of the ilium
is called the iliac crest.

The bottom part of the pelvis
at the front is called the pubes,
the shame bone.

The place where the two sides
of the pelvis come together in the
front is called the pubic symphysis.

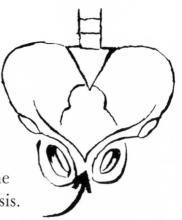

The inside hollow is called
the iliac fossa.

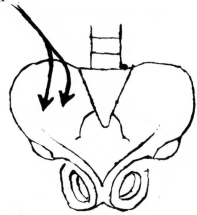

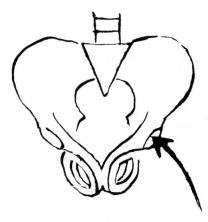

The sockets for the femur
are called the acetabulum.

The back part of the
bottom is the ischium
(pronounced ish ee yum).

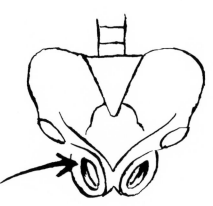

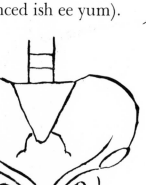

And the rough knobs are called
the ischial tuberosities.

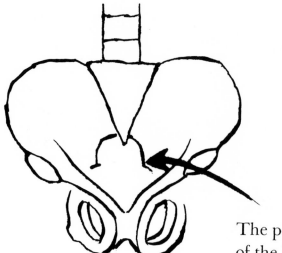

The points at the inside base of the back are called the iliac spines.

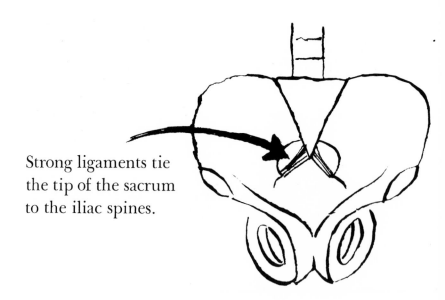

Strong ligaments tie the tip of the sacrum to the iliac spines.

THE RIBS

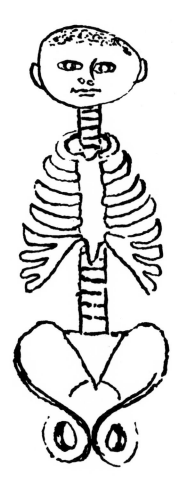

Along the spine, between the skull
and the pelvis, are the ribs.

The ribs lie under the chest.
The chest is square, like a chest.

But without shoulders,
the chest, or thorax,

would be like a lamp shade,
flattened a bit from front to back

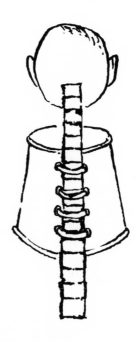

and tied to the
vertebral column in back.

The rib cage is cut away in front like a suit coat.

The breast bone, or sternum, is in the middle of the front.

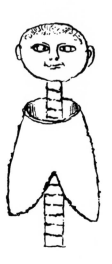

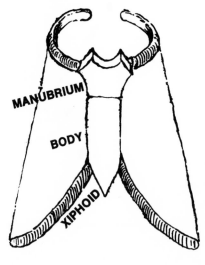

The sternum is like a dagger. It has three parts: the manubrium or handle, the body, and the xiphoid.

Most of the ribs circle
between the vertebral column
and the sternum.

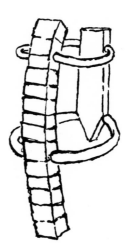

But the ribs at the bottom
do not reach the sternum.
Some of the lower ribs hang
on to each other.
But the last two don't make
even this, so they hang free.

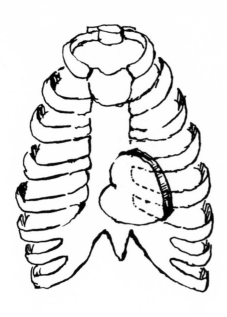

The ribs, or thoracic cage,
protect the heart and lungs.

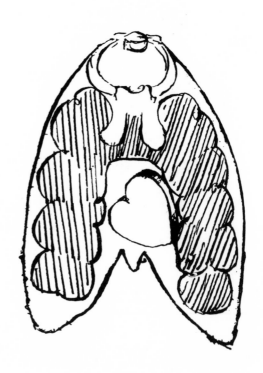

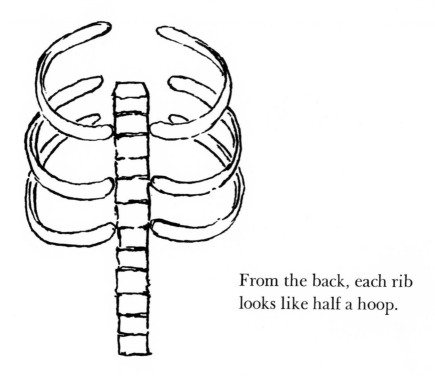

From the back, each rib
looks like half a hoop.

The back end of each rib is pointed and
sticks in a notch between two vertebrae,
right on the intervertebral disc.

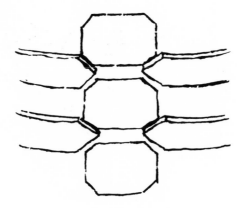

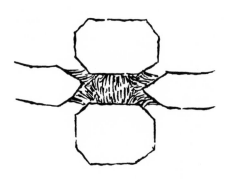

The rib tip fibers blend with the disc.

A transverse process braces each rib.

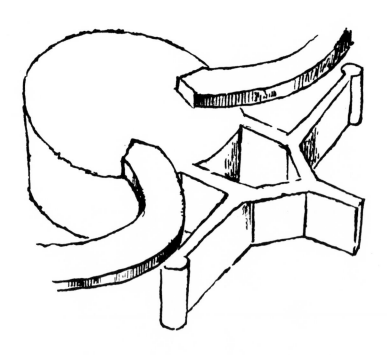

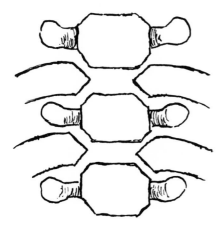

In back, the ribs slant down.

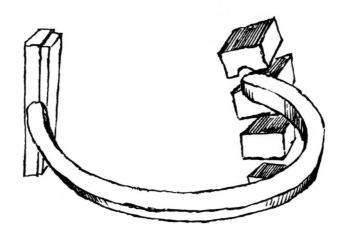

From the side, you can see the ribs slant
down, just as a bucket handle does.

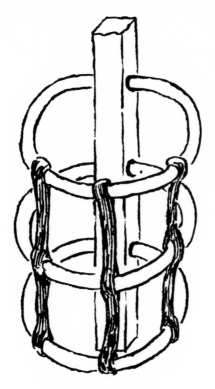

If the ribs were a series of hoops tied
together and looped through a post,
the space they enclosed would get bigger
when the hoops were raised.

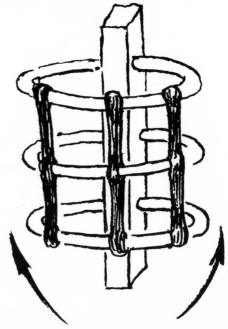

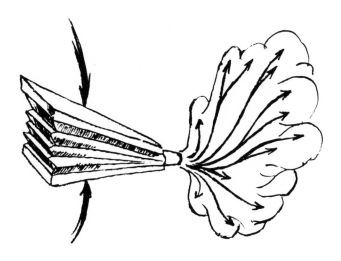

They would be like a bellows, which
pushed down, folds in and squeezes out
air, then pulled out, unfolds, gets
bigger and sucks in air.

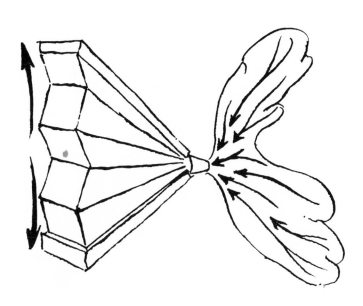

Bellows and hoops both resemble the ribs.

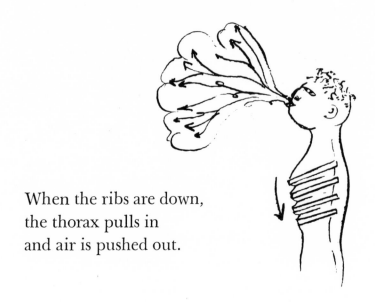

When the ribs are down,
the thorax pulls in
and air is pushed out.

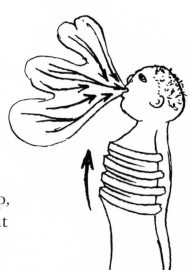

When the ribs are up,
the thorax pushes out
and air is sucked in.

Here is the thorax from the back:

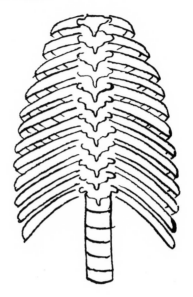

And here it is from the front:

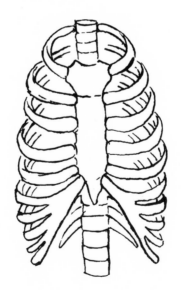

Man's shape is progressing. When the thoracic cage and pelvic bucket are added to the spine, he begins to look almost human. But more is still needed to make him into the man we know. For one thing, he needs arms.

The arms fit onto triangular shoulder blades or scapulae, which rest across the back, on top of the thorax, anchored only by muscles.

The shoulder blade has a small socket at the outer corner called the glenoid fossa (a glen is a valley or hollow).

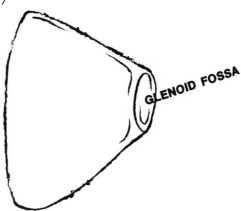

GLENOID FOSSA

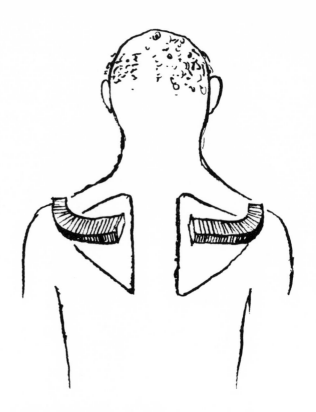

Across the back of the scapula runs a ridge,
the scapular spine.

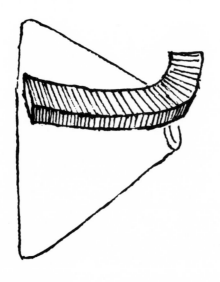

It curves over the top
of the glenoid fossa.

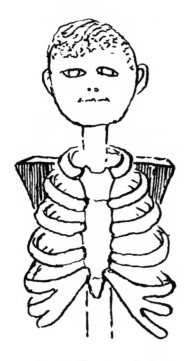

The scapula sticks out from either side of the thorax at the back.

A small part of the scapular spine called the acromion process (or bump) curves around toward the front of the thorax.

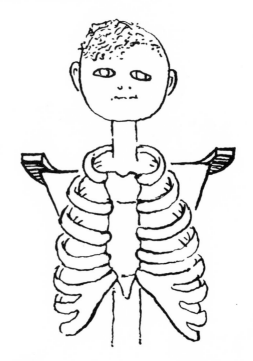

A brace runs from the acromion process
to the manubrium (the top of the sternum).

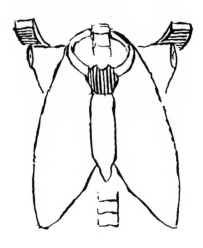

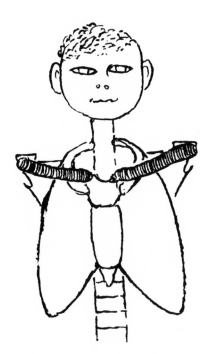

This brace is called the
collarbone or clavicle.

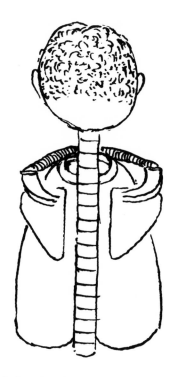

A back view of the scapula, acromion process,
and clavicle on both sides shows that they
make a kind of oval.

The same thing is evident from the top.

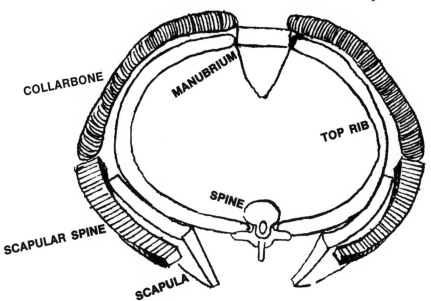

COLLARBONE

MANUBRIUM

TOP RIB

SPINE

SCAPULAR SPINE

SCAPULA

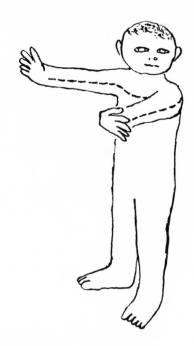

If you could see a cross section of the bones of a man in this position, you would see that the clavicles function as a brace for the scapulae.

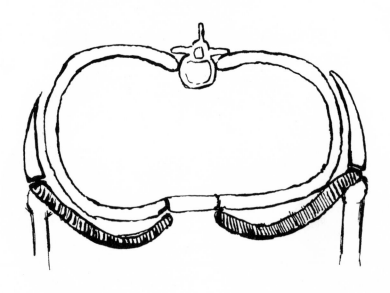

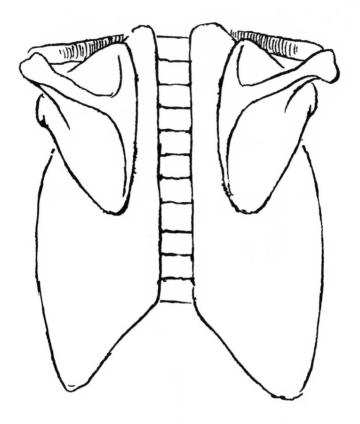

The scapula and the clavicle, plastered
against the back, make the bony shoulder,
the first part of the arm.

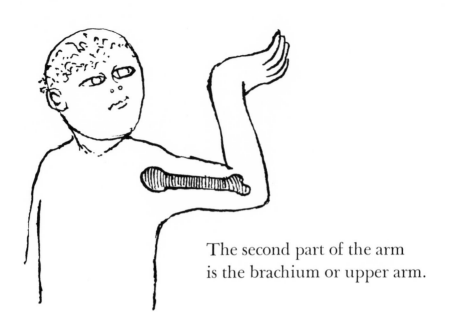

The second part of the arm
is the brachium or upper arm.

This bone, the humerus, has a big
ball on one end. It fits into a
small socket, the glenoid fossa.

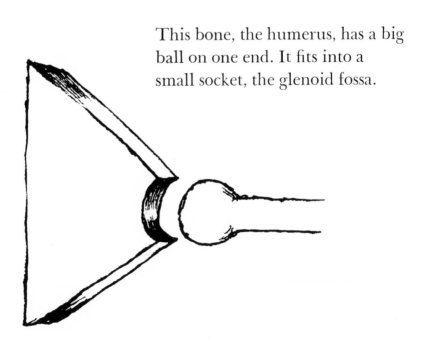

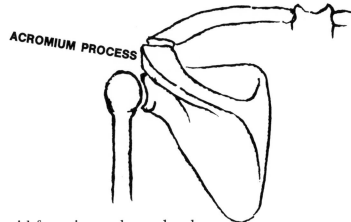

ACROMIUM PROCESS

The glenoid fossa is overhung by the
acromion process and the clavicle.

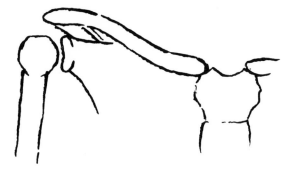

These two guard the joint on top to
keep the head of the humerus from being
pushed up out of the glenoid cavity.

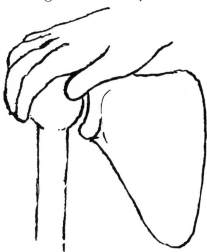

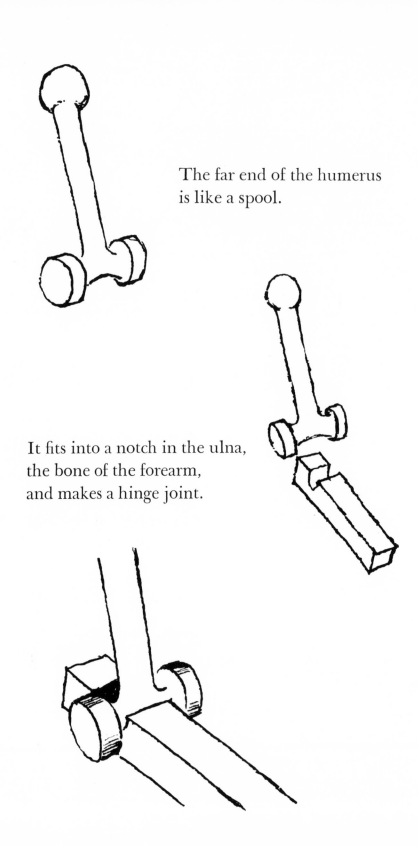

The far end of the humerus is like a spool.

It fits into a notch in the ulna, the bone of the forearm, and makes a hinge joint.

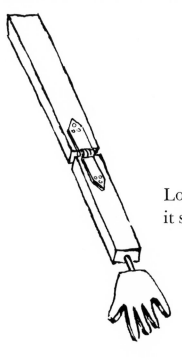

Looking at the joint as a real hinge,
it seems to bend into a bow shape,

like an L—L-bow—elbow.

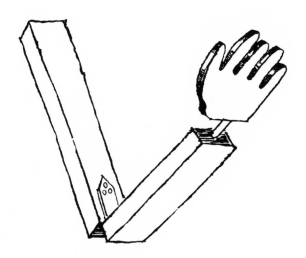

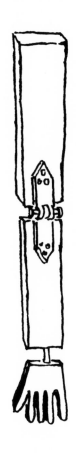

Put the hand on a spindle
so it can turn;

add a handle, the radius,
to turn the hand.

Extend the radius to the elbow,

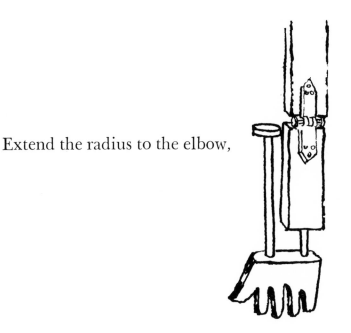

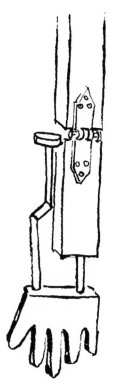

and put a bend in the
radius so the handle
end will stay in place
when the hand end moves.

Next modify the humerus
to make room for the radius.

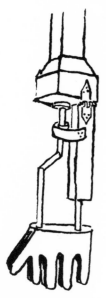

Tie the head of the radius
to the ulna with a loop.

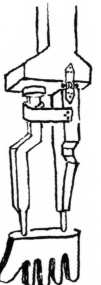

And cut away part of the ulna
so it fits in with the radius.

But, of course, the elbow is not a real
hinge at all. It is a spool and notch.

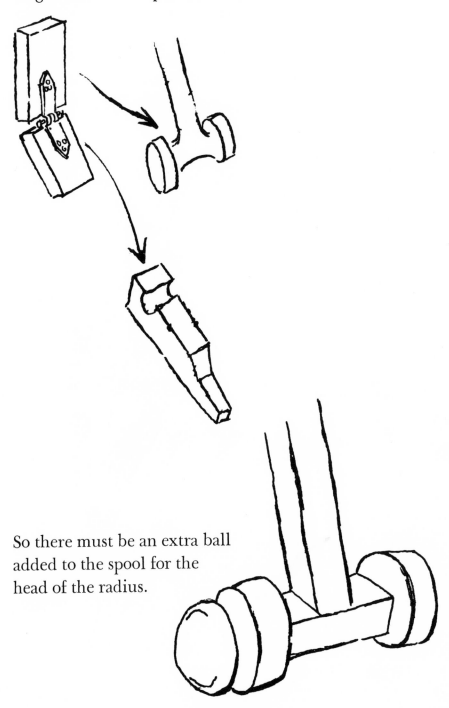

So there must be an extra ball
added to the spool for the
head of the radius.

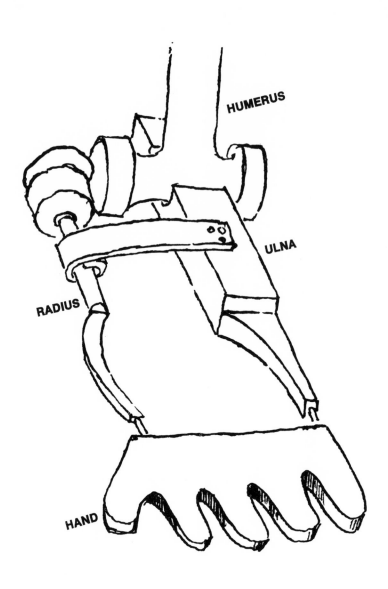

With this we have a pretty fair
working model of the elbow.

THE WRIST and HAND

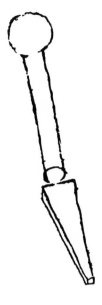

The ulna is the main bone at the elbow.

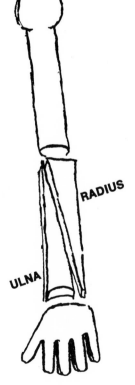

The radius is the main bone at the wrist.

The radius and ulna together
made a half-circle socket for
the wrist bones to fit into.

The carpus, or wrist, is
curved at the top to fit into
the socket of the forearm.

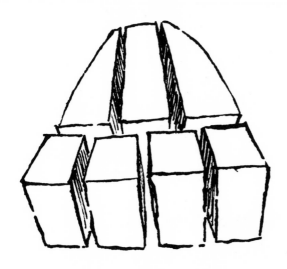

The wrist is made of seven bones,
with the entire structure curved up at
the sides in the shape of a shovel.

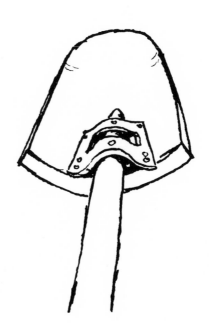

The hollow is roofed over by a tough ligament.

The area between the ligament and the bone contains a supply tunnel for the hand.

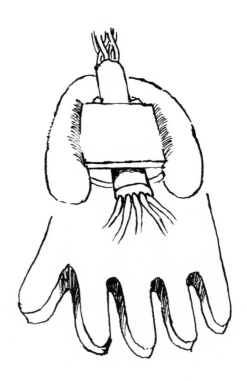

When the wrist bends up or down,
bending occurs at the radiocarpal
joint and at the mid-carpal joint.

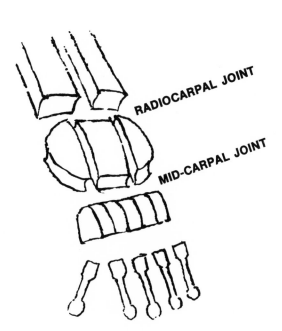

But when the wrist moves from side to side,
the carpus moves as a rigid unit.

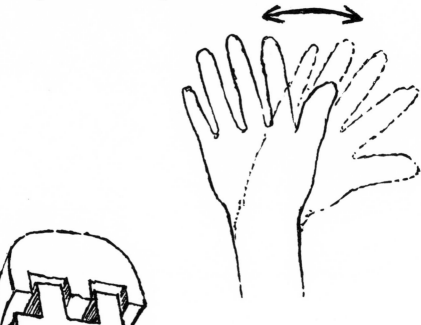

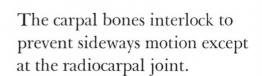

The carpal bones interlock to
prevent sideways motion except
at the radiocarpal joint.

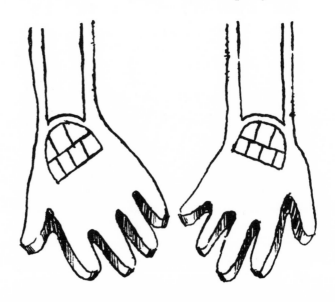

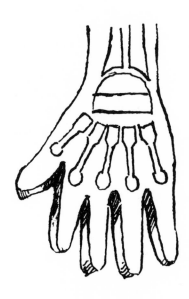

The carpals are followed by the metacarpals,
and they by the fingers or phalanges.

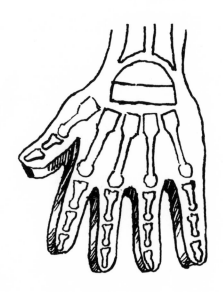

The hand is like a Chinese fan.

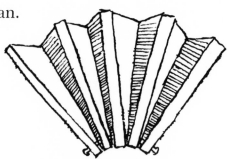

Opening and closing this fan occurs
at the finger, the phalangeal, level.

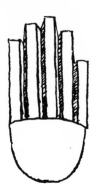

Bending the fan (bringing the thumb into
opposition) occurs at the carpometacarpal level.

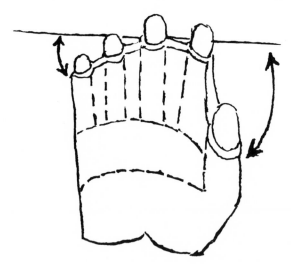

Therefore, to review:

The upper arm or brachium
has but one bone.

The forearm has two bones.

The wrist or carpal bones
are in two rows:
the first row has three bones;*
the second row has four bones.

(*Commonly the first row is said to
be four in number. However, the fourth
bone is a sesamoid bone—that is,
one which develops in the tendon.)

The palm of the hand has
five bones, five metacarpals.

And, of course, there are five fingers.

Each finger has three bones, but
the thumb has only two.

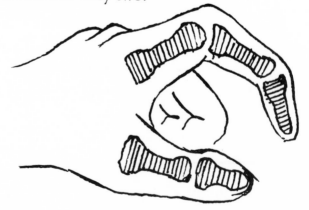

THE LEG

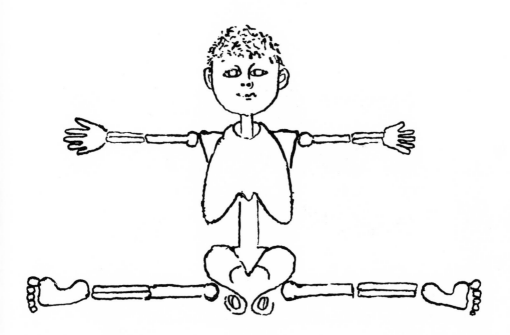

If you could see an unborn baby, you would
see that at first the legs and arms
are very much alike in appearance. The
developing arms and legs are symmetrical.

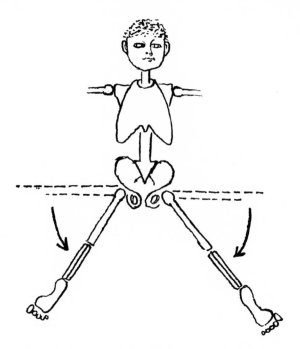

Then the legs swing down and rotate to
bring the soles of the feet to the
ground, with the feet facing forward.

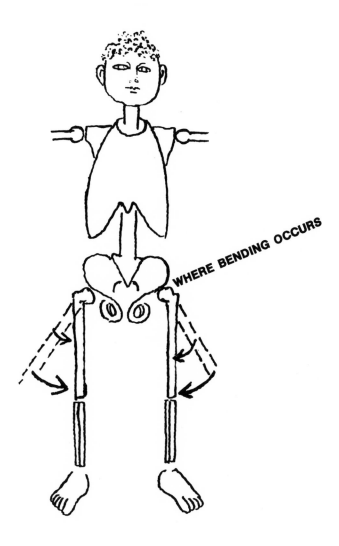

WHERE BENDING OCCURS

The upper leg bone or femur bends at the
hip level. This lets the feet and legs come
together so that we are not bowlegged
and walk on parallel legs.

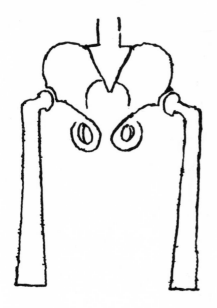

The femur is like a cane.
The head is rounded
and the shaft is straight.

In walking, the ball head rotates
back and forth in the hip socket,
a part of the pelvis.

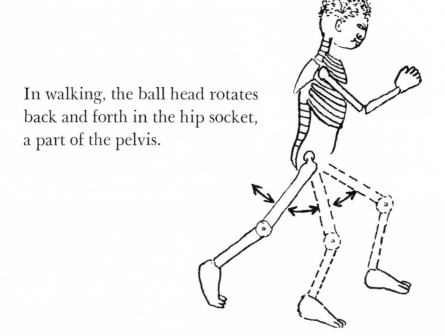

There are two rockers protruding
from the lower end of the femur,

and two corresponding depressions
on the upper end of the bone below,
the shin bone, or tibia.

The inner rocker or condyle
is deeper than the outer,
because the femur and tibia come together
at a slant. The difference in the condyles
is just enough to make sure that the leg bones
from the knee down are really parallel.

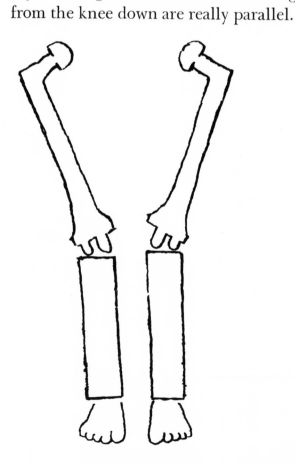

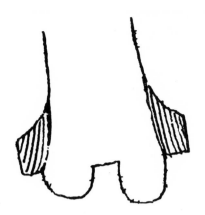

The lower end of the femur
flares out above the condyles.
This is epi—or above the condyles—epicondyles.

Here's a 3-dimensional view of the knee.

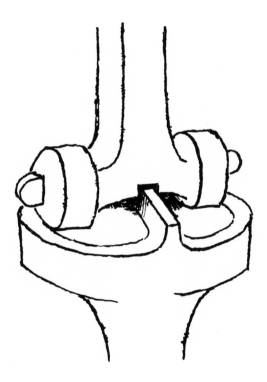

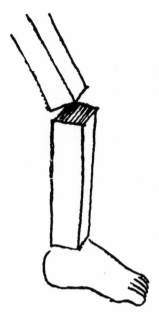

The knee joint bends backward, but not forward.

Strong straps, the collateral ligaments, keep it from moving forward.

Knee bent, ligaments loose.

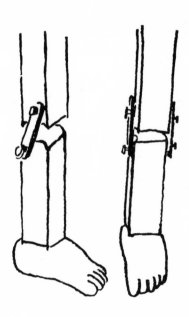

Knee straight, ligaments tight.

Big muscles pull
on the tibia.

When the knee is bent, the
muscle rubs over the joint.

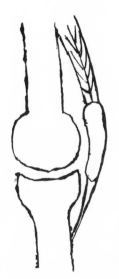

To prevent damage to
the muscle, we have a
kneecap, the patella.

It protects the muscle
from the knee joint.

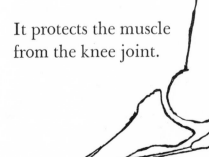

This is the patella
seen from the front.

THE ANKLE and FOOT

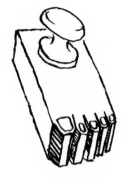

At the bottom of the tibia is the foot, the top of which sticks up like a round knob.

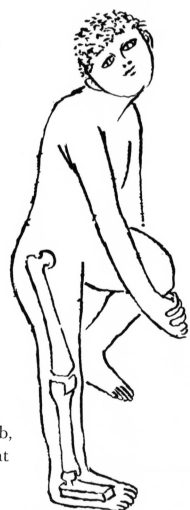

The tibia rests on the knob, and alone bears the weight of the body.

But the tibia and the knob do not complete
the ankle. Another bone, the fibula, is
needed. Fibula means "little pin."

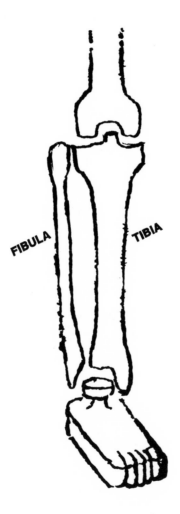

Together, the tibia and fibula form
an arch over the knob of the foot.

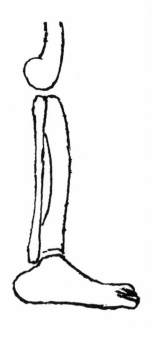

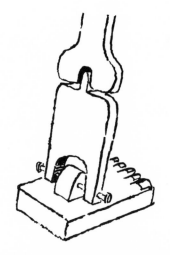

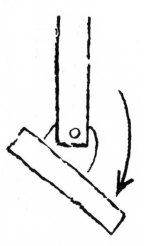

Because they form this type
of joint, the ankle can move
up and down, but can move
very little from side to side.

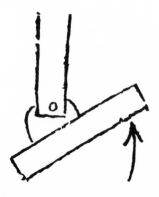

The first bone of the ankle
is shaped like the head of
a mechanic's hammer.
It is called the talus.

Just next to it, forming the upper part of
the foot, is the saucer-shaped navicular.

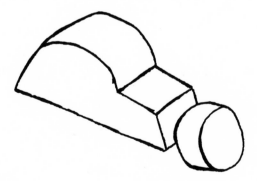

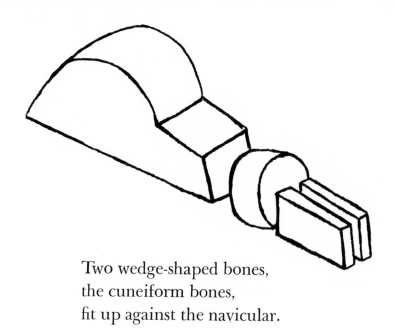

Two wedge-shaped bones,
the cuneiform bones,
fit up against the navicular.

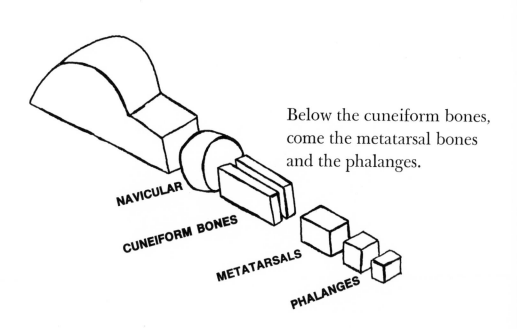

Below the cuneiform bones,
come the metatarsal bones
and the phalanges.

NAVICULAR

CUNEIFORM BONES

METATARSALS

PHALANGES

Another bone supports the back of the
foot, the heel bone. It raises the foot in
the rear, fits below the talus, and
is called the calcaneus.

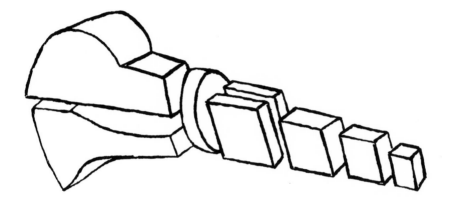

This is how a foot looks from the
big toe, or medial, side.

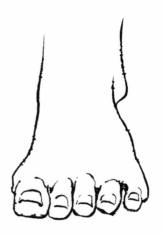

On the lateral, or little toe, side, there is
the cuneiform bone, and another bone called the
cuboid. On this side, the calcaneus sticks
out beyond the talus as far as the end
of the navicular. The third cuneiform bone
and the cuboid lie parallel to the other
two cuneiform bones.

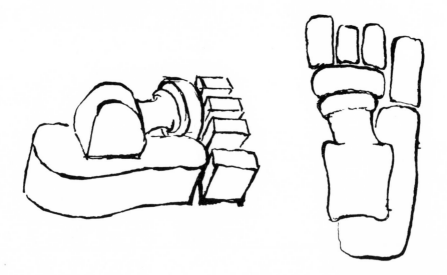

Looking down on the foot from above,

there are three cuneiforms and a cuboid below the navicular and the calcaneus,

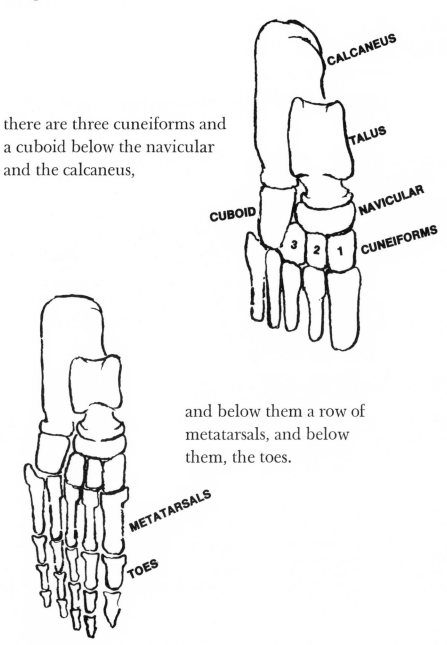

and below them a row of metatarsals, and below them, the toes.

Here is a three-dimensional diagram of the foot.

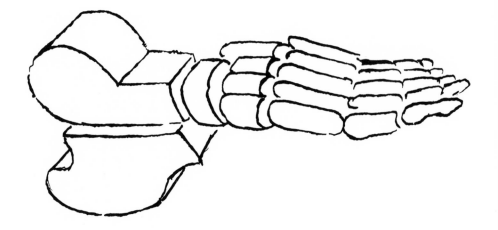

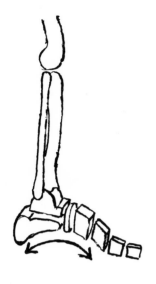

The bones of the foot act
like a spring lengthwise.

The metatarsals make
a cross arch.

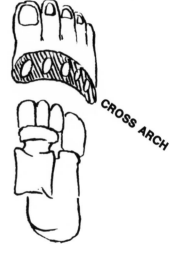

CROSS ARCH

So weight is borne in
the foot on three points.

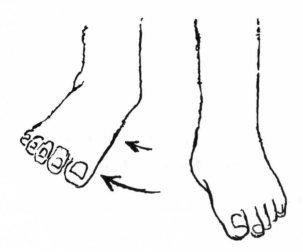

The foot can be bent from side to side
because of a joint between the talus,
the calcaneus, and the navicular.

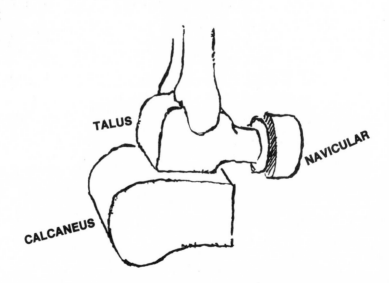

TALUS

NAVICULAR

CALCANEUS

The head of the first metatarsal takes
the strain when we stand on our toes.

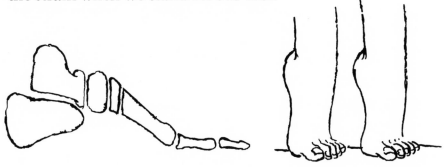

In walking we push
with our big toes.

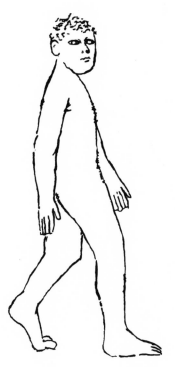

THE SKULL

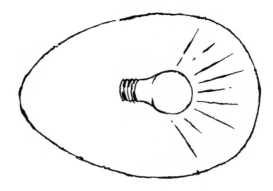

At the other end of the body from the toes
is the skull. From the side, the top
of the skull, the part that holds the brain,
is shaped like an eggshell.
Except that it is flattened on the bottom.

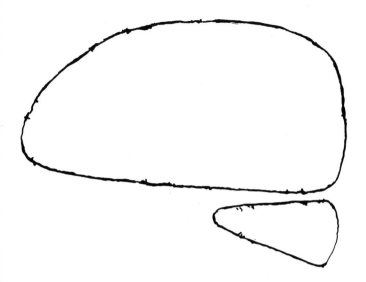

The cone-shaped eye sockets are underneath.

The nose fits between
the eye sockets.

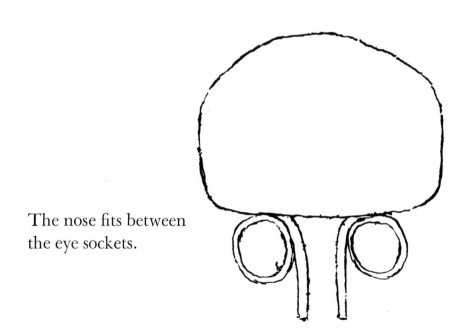

If you cut off the top

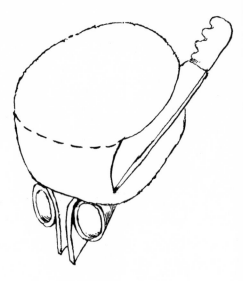

and the front of the skull,

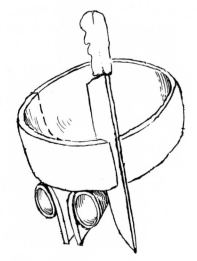

it is clear that the walls of
the eye sockets form the side
walls of the nose.

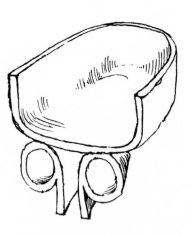

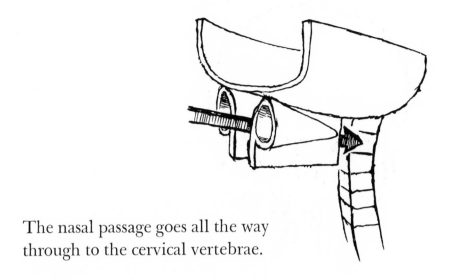

The nasal passage goes all the way
through to the cervical vertebrae.

The passage is divided into two parts
by a wall or septum in the middle.

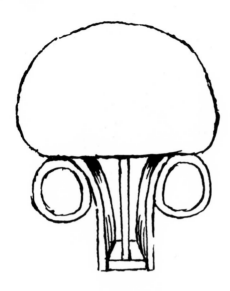

A bony floor, the palate, separates
the nose from the mouth.

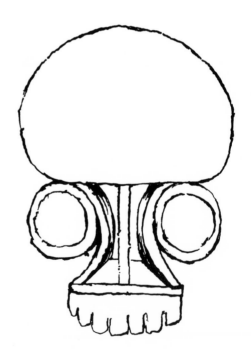

It also anchors the upper teeth.

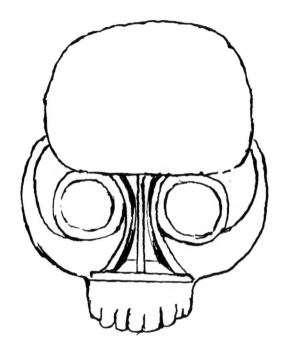

A brace runs from the corner of each eye socket to the side of the skull. These are the cheek bones or zygomatic arches.

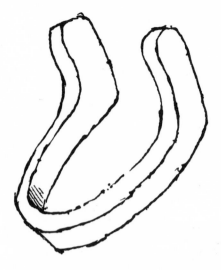

The lower jaw is shaped like a horseshoe,
with the ends bent upwards.

The lower teeth fit into the lower jaw.

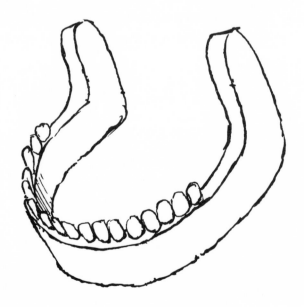

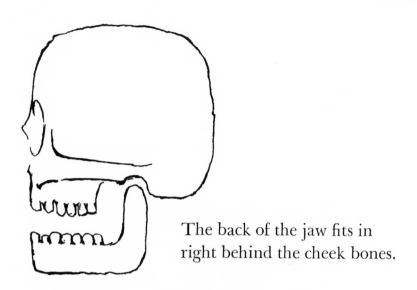

The back of the jaw fits in right behind the cheek bones.

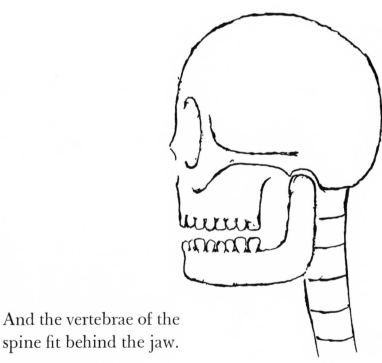

And the vertebrae of the spine fit behind the jaw.

And here is the outside of the skull
—all finished.

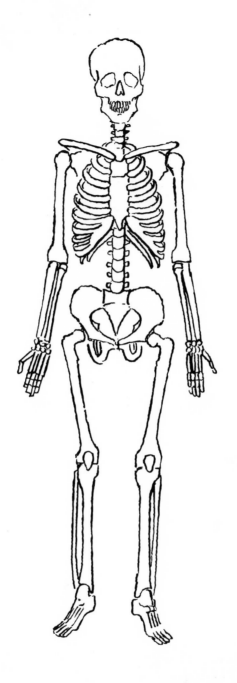

And this is a finished man, his skeleton at
least, from his toes to the top of his skull.

INDEX

INDEX